EASY
STREET

BY RITA GRAY

ILLUSTRATIONS BY MARY BONO

· DUTTON CHILDREN'S BOOKS ·

DUTTON CHILDREN'S BOOKS
A division of Penguin Young Readers Group

Published by the Penguin Group
Penguin Group (USA) Inc., 375 Hudson Street, New York, New York 10014, U.S.A. • Penguin Group (Canada), 90 Eglinton
Avenue, Suite 700, Toronto, Ontario, Canada M4P 2Y3 (a division of Pearson Penguin Canada Inc.) • Penguin Books Ltd,
80 Strand, London WC2R 0RL, England • Penguin Ireland, 25 St Stephen's Green, Dublin 2, Ireland (a division of Penguin
Books Ltd) • Penguin Group (Australia), 250 Camberwell Road, Camberwell, Victoria 3124, Australia (a division of
Pearson Australia Group Pty Ltd) • Penguin Books India Pvt Ltd, 11 Community Centre, Panchsheel Park, New Delhi—110
017, India • Penguin Group (NZ), Cnr Airborne and Rosedale Roads, Albany, Auckland 1310, New Zealand (a division of
Pearson New Zealand Ltd) • Penguin Books (South Africa) (Pty) Ltd, 24 Sturdee Avenue, Rosebank, Johannesburg 2196,
South Africa • Penguin Books Ltd, Registered Offices: 80 Strand, London WC2R 0RL, England

Text copyright © 2006 by Rita Gray
Illustrations copyright © 2006 by Mary Bono
All rights reserved.

CIP DATA IS AVAILABLE

Published in the United States by Dutton Children's Books,
a division of Penguin Young Readers Group
345 Hudson Street, New York, New York 10014
www.penguin.com/youngreaders

Manufactured in China • First Edition
ISBN 0-525-47657-1
Special Markets ISBN 978-0-525-47926-0 Not for Resale
3 5 7 9 10 8 6 4 2

This Imagination Library edition is published by Penguin Group (USA), a Pearson
company, exclusively for Dolly Parton's Imagination Library, a not-for-profit
program designed to inspire a love of reading and learning, sponsored in part by The
Dollywood Foundation. Penguin's trade editions of this work are available wherever
books are sold.

Special thanks to Mr. John Farrell for paving the way for this project. Mr. Farrell has been the Superintendent of Highways for the town of Hunter, New York, for the past fifteen years.

To my nephews, Eddie, Marshall, and Teddy
—R.G.

For Darius, Leyla, and Glenn
—M.B.

Make a street, make a street, workers in a row.

Make me a street for things that go.

Smooth out the dirt with a big metal blade.

Pack it down, before it's paved.

Roll it, roll it, wheels so fat.

Roll it down to make it flat.

Use big rocks. Chop, chop, chop!

Fill a dump truck to the top.

Spread the gravel, rough and tough.

Spread until you have enough.

Roll it, roll it, wheels so fat.

Roll it down to make it flat.

Asphalt, asphalt, cooked with heat.

Pouring out a slice of street.

Sticky street, soft to spread.

Squeeze it out like jam on bread.

Roll it, roll it, wheels so fat.

Roll it down to make it flat.

One more layer, shiny black.

Then . . .

. . . a roller comes right back. Roll it, roll it,

wheels so fat. Roll it down to make it flat.

Bring a truck to paint long lines.

Don't forget . . .

. . . to post some signs.

A job well done!

Call it a day. Get your wheels and drive away . . .

. . . on Easy Street. BEEP! BEEP!

Easy Street is a recipe for just one type of street, using asphalt. The thing all streets have in common is that they are made of layers. Each layer must be packed down, or "compacted," before the next layer can be applied. Compacting each layer makes it firm, and also causes all the layers to bind together into one solid slab of street.

Asphalt presents a special challenge, since it hardens as it cools and must be spread and compacted while still warm. Dump trucks arrive at the work site to deposit hot asphalt into the asphalt-paving machine. This hot asphalt is then squeezed out onto the roadbed in one long, continuous layer.

Once the paving process begins, it must proceed at a steady pace. When the paver starts running low on its load of hot asphalt, another dump truck gives it a quick refill. Compactors must follow the paver at a close distance in order to compact the still-warm asphalt. This will produce a street that is strong and free of bumps and seams. Additional workers may follow on foot to shovel up unwanted asphalt spills and to smooth out rough edges.

The word *asphalt* comes from the Greek word *asphaltos,* which means "secure." The asphalt we use to pave modern streets is 95 percent aggregate (crushed stones, gravel, and sand) and 5 percent asphalt cement, made from petroleum. These ingredients are heated and mixed at an asphalt plant until all the rough stuff is well coated.

Asphalt is also a naturally occurring material that comes from inside the earth. Millions of years ago, when asphalt bubbled up to the earth's surface, it caused rainwater to collect, forming miniature lakes. Unsuspecting dinosaurs came to drink at these water holes and became trapped in the hidden black goo. Petroleum, the ingredient we now use to make asphalt, is made of decomposed prehistoric plant and animal life. This is why petroleum is called a "fossil fuel." So the roads you travel on every day are actually held together with dinosaur glue!